MW00997830

The route to your rٍٍٍ.ٍ

When they look back at their formative years, many Indians nostalgically recall the vital part Amar Chitra Katha picture books have played in their lives. It was **ACK – Amar Chitra Katha** – that first gave them a glimpse of their glorious heritage.

Since they were introduced in 1967, there are now **over 400 Amar Chitra Katha** titles to choose from. **Over 90 million copies** have been sold worldwide.

Now the Amar Chitra Katha titles are even more widely available in **1000+ bookstores all across India**. Log on to www.ack-media.com to locate a bookstore near you. If you do not have access to a bookstore, you can buy all the titles through our online store **www.amarchitrakatha.com**. We provide quick delivery anywhere in the world.

To make it easy for you to locate the titles of your choice from our treasure trove of titles, the books are now arranged in five categories.

Epics and Mythology
Best known stories from the Epics and the Puranas

Indian Classics
Enchanting tales from Indian literature

Fables and Humour
Evergreen folktales, legends and tales of wisdom and humour

Bravehearts
Stirring tales of brave men and women of India

Visionaries
Inspiring tales of thinkers, social reformers and nation builders

Contemporary Classics
The Best of Modern Indian literature

Amar Chitra Katha Pvt Ltd
© Amar Chitra Katha Pvt Ltd, 1998, Reprinted March 2014, ISBN 978-81-905990-7-8
Published by Amar Chitra Katha Pvt. Ltd., Krishna House, 3rd Floor,
Raghuvanshi Mill Compound, S.B.Marg, Lower Parel (W), Mumbai- 400 013. India
Printed at Asha Printery 225/A-1, Shah & Nahar Industrial Estate, Dhanraj Mills Compound,
Sitaram Jadhav Marg, Lower Parel, Mumbai - 400013
For Consumer Complaints Contact Tel : +91-22 40497436
Email: customerservice@ack-media.com

The route to your roots

THE JACKAL AND
THE WARDRUM

A hungry jackal finds food when he overcomes fear. A curious monkey meddles with something that does not concern him and comes to a sticky end. Philosophy, psychology, politics and human relations become simple enough to be understood by a child in Pandit Vishnu Sharma's brilliant work, the Panchatantra. Written and compiled in around 200 BC, every story is as relevant today as it was in ancient times.

Script	Illustrations	Editor
G.L.Chandiramani	Jeffrey Fowler	Anant Pai

THE JACKAL AND THE WAR DRUM.

GOMAYA THE JACKAL HAD NOT EATEN FOR MANY DAYS AND WAS VERY HUNGRY.

IF I DON'T FIND SOME FOOD SOON, I WILL DIE.

AS HE WANDERED THROUGH THE FOREST IN SEARCH OF FOOD HE CAME UPON AN OLD BATTLEFIELD.

WHAT'S THAT NOISE ? I'D BETTER RUN BEFORE I'M ATTACKED.

WHIR WHOOSH

WHIR ! WHOOSH !

ZOOM

NO! I WON'T RUN. I'LL BE BRAVE AND FIND OUT WHO'S MAKING THE NOISE.

SCREEEECH

SO HE CREPT BACK TRYING TO BE BRAVE.

WHIR! WHOOSH

TO HIS ASTONISHMENT GOMAYA FOUND THAT THE NOISE CAME FROM A HARMLESS OLD WAR DRUM.

WHIR! WHOOSH!

THE LOW BRANCHES OF A TREE WERE SWISHING AGAINST IT AND MAKING THE NOISE. NEAR THE DRUM THERE WAS PLENTY OF FOOD.

WHIR! WHOOSH!

WHIR! WHOOSH!

WHAT A FOOL I'D HAVE BEEN IF I'D LET A SILLY OLD WAR DRUM CHEAT ME OF ALL THIS DELICIOUS FOOD!

MORALS: FEAR OF THE UNKNOWN BRINGS NO GAIN.

THE COBRA AND THE CROW

Once, there lived a pair of crows on an old tree. In the hollow of the same tree there lived a wicked cobra.

EVERY TIME I LAY EGGS, THIS WICKED COBRA EATS THEM ALL UP. WHAT SHALL WE DO?

LET'S ASK OUR FRIEND, THE JACKAL. HE'S A CLEVER FELLOW.

SAY FRIEND, THERE'S A BAD OLD COBRA WHO LIVES IN OUR TREE. HE EATS ALL OUR CHILDREN. HOW CAN WE GET RID OF HIM AND PROTECT OUR HOME?

JJACKAL

THE JACKAL THOUGHT FOR A WHILE.

THEN —

I'LL TELL YOU HOW. LISTEN TO ME CAREFULLY. B..z..z..z....

ACCORDING TO PLAN, THE CROWS FLEW OVER A LAKE WHERE THE QUEEN AND HER MAIDS WERE BATHING. THEY HAD LEFT THEIR CLOTHES AND JEWELRY ON THE BANK OF THE LAKE.

NOW YOU KNOW WHAT TO DO.

THE FEMALE CROW SWOOPED DOWN, PICKED UP A GOLD NECKLACE AND FLEW OFF.

FLAP!

FLAP!

SOME OF THE KING'S SERVANTS, WHO WERE WORKING NEARBY, HEARD THE WOMEN SHOUTING. THEY BEGAN CHASING THE CROW.

SHE FLEW OVER THE HOME OF THE BAD COBRA AND DROPPED THE NECKLACE NEARBY.

THE COBRA CAME OUT...

... AND THE ANGRY SERVANTS SAW HIM.

Kill him! KILL HIM!

BAM THUD

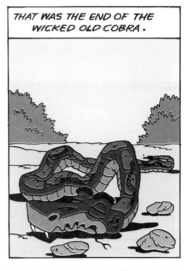

THAT WAS THE END OF THE WICKED OLD COBRA.

THE MEN GOT BACK THE GOLD CHAIN AND THE CROWS LIVED HAPPILY EVER AFTER.

MORAL : MIGHTY BRAWN IS NO MATCH FOR NIMBLE BRAIN.

THE TURTLE WHO FELL OFF A STICK.

NEAR A CERTAIN LAKE THERE LIVED A TURTLE AND TWO SWANS. THEY SPENT MOST OF THEIR TIME IN TELLING EACH OTHER STORIES.

AND SO IT CAME TO PASS...

SO THE YEARS PASSED. THEN SUDDENLY ONE YEAR THERE WAS A DROUGHT.

THE LAKE IS ALMOST DRY. HOW CAN WE LIVE WITHOUT WATER?

DON'T WORRY. WE WILL FIND A WAY OUT.

SUDDENLY THE TURTLE HAD AN IDEA.

FIRST FIND A LAKE FULL OF WATER. THEN BRING ME A STICK. I'LL HOLD ON TO THE MIDDLE OF IT. YOU HOLD THE ENDS AND CARRY ME TO OUR NEW LAKE.

GOOD, BUT WHILE WE ARE FLYING, TAKE CARE THAT YOU DON'T OPEN YOUR MOUTH.

MORAL : SILENCE IS GOLDEN.

THE MONKEY AND THE LOG.

ONCE, CERTAIN WORKMEN WERE BUSY BUILDING A TEMPLE ON THE OUTSKIRTS OF A TOWN.

WHEN IT WAS NOON —

LET US GO TO THE TOWN FOR LUNCH.

I'LL JUST PUT A WEDGE HERE AND COME.

I HOPE NO ONE TOUCHES THAT WEDGE WHILE WE ARE AWAY.

HARDLY HAD THE WORKMEN LEFT, WHEN A GROUP OF MONKEYS ARRIVED ON THE SCENE.

ONE OF THEM PERCHED HIMSELF ON THE HALF-SAWN LOG.

WHAT IS THIS PIECE OF WOOD DOING HERE?

I WONDER WHAT WILL HAPPEN IF I PULL IT OUT?

SO HE PULLED AT THE WEDGE.

UGH! IT'S TOUGH · ·

OUT IT CAME.

HELP

THE GAP CLOSED IN, TRAPPING THE MONKEY'S LEG.

SNAP

THE POOR MONKEY WAS INSTANTLY KILLED.

MORAL : DO NOT MEDDLE WITH THINGS THAT DO NOT CONCERN YOU.

A MERCHANT AND A KING'S SERVANT.

ONCE UPON A TIME, IN A CITY CALLED VARDHAMANA —

HE IS WISE AND GOOD TOO!

ONCE AGAIN DANTILA HAS PROVED HIMSELF TO BE AN EXCELLENT ADMINISTRATOR.

WHILE THE PEOPLE WERE PRAISING HIM, DANTILA WAS BUSY TALKING WITH HIS WIFE ABOUT THEIR DAUGHTER'S WEDDING.

I HAVE INVITED THE KING, THE QUEEN, AND THE ENTIRE COURT FOR THE WEDDING.

WE'D BETTER START THE PREPARATIONS. THERE ARE HARDLY A FEW DAYS LEFT.

ON THE WEDDING DAY —

WELCOME, O KING. I AM HIGHLY HONOURED BY YOUR PRESENCE TODAY.

GORAMBA THE KING'S SWEEPER CAME TO THE WEDDING, TOO, BUT UNINVITED.

DANTILA WAS FURIOUS.

GET OUT, GORAMBA! HOW DARE YOU COME HERE?

I'LL GET EVEN WITH HIM SOMEHOW.

THE WHOLE OF THAT NIGHT HE THOUGHT ABOUT IT.

AT LAST JUST BEFORE SUNRISE —

I'VE GOT IT!

THAT MORNING WHEN GORAMBA WENT TO SWEEP THE KING'S CHAMBER —

SHAME ON DANTILA! HOW DARE HE EMBRACE THE QUEEN!

GORAMBA, WHAT WERE YOU SAYING? TELL ME AT ONCE, IS IT TRUE?

MASTER! PLEASE! I WAS GAMBLING ALL NIGHT. NOW I'M HALF ASLEEP AND I DON'T KNOW WHAT I'M SAYING.

GORAMBA MOVES FREELY IN THE PALACE. MAYBE HE REALLY SAW IT HAPPEN.

THE KING DRESSED AND SENT FOR HIS CHIEF GUARD.

HENCEFORTH, DANTILA SHALL NOT ENTER THE PALACE GATES.

YES, YOUR MAJESTY.

THE NEXT DAY DANTILA WANTED TO MEET THE KING. BUT—

WHY.. B..BUT... I-I-I...

HA! HA! HA!

SORRY YOU MAY NOT ENTER. THE KING'S ORDERS.

NOW I KNOW WHO CAUSED THE TROUBLE! A KING'S SERVANT HIGH OR LOW, MUST INDEED BE RESPECTED.

THAT VERY EVENING DANTILA INVITED GORAMBA TO HIS HOME.

MY FRIEND, PLEASE ACCEPT THESE GIFTS AND FORGIVE ME FOR MY BEHAVIOUR THAT DAY.

THANK YOU SIR, THANK YOU.

I FORGIVE YOU. AND YOU WILL SEE AGAIN HOW CLEVER I CAN BE.

THE NEXT MORNING GORAMBA WAS SWEEPING THE KING'S ROOM AS USUAL.

HO! HO! HA! HA! OUR KING EATS CUCUMBERS IN THE LAVATORY.

MORAL : EVERY DOG HAS ITS DAY.

THE MERCHANT'S SON AND THE IRON BALANCE.

IN A CERTAIN TOWN, THERE LIVED A MERCHANT CALLED JWEERNADHANA.

I HAVE LOST ALL MY MONEY IN BUSINESS HERE. LET ME TRY MY LUCK IN SOME OTHER TOWN.

BEFORE LEAVING HE VISITED ANOTHER MERCHANT, A FRIEND.

FRIEND, WILL YOU KEEP THIS IRON BALANCE FOR ME TILL I RETURN?

I WILL!

JWEERNADHANA SET OUT ON HIS JOURNEY.

I HOPE I COME BACK RICH!

AFTER A FEW MONTHS JWEERNADHANA RETURNED AND WENT TO MEET HIS FRIEND.

FRIEND, I HAVE COME FOR MY BALANCE.

I'M SORRY. THE RATS ATE IT UP.

JWEERNADHANA KNEW THAT HIS FRIEND WAS LYING. BUT WHAT COULD HE DO?

THEN SUDDENLY HE HAD AN IDEA.

WELL! FRIEND. I CAN'T BLAME YOU. ANYWAY I'LL GO FOR A BATH. CAN YOU SEND YOUR LITTLE SON WITH ME TO HELP ME CARRY MY BELONGINGS?

SURE. WHY NOT!

SO THE LITTLE BOY ACCOMPANIED JWEERNADHANA AND CARRIED HIS BELONGINGS FOR HIM.

ON THE WAY THEY CAME UPON A CAVE.

LET'S ENTER IT AND SEE WHAT IT'S LIKE INSIDE.

ONCE INSIDE, JWEERNADHANA LEFT THE BOY AND QUICKLY RAN OUT.

THEN HE BLOCKED THE ENTRANCE WITH A HUGE BOULDER.

WELL! NOW THE BOY CAN'T COME OUT.

THEN HE RETURNED TO HIS FRIEND.

WHY ARE YOU ALONE? WHERE IS MY LITTLE SON?

I'M SORRY, FRIEND. A FLAMINGO PICKED HIM UP AND FLEW OFF.

WHAT! YOU LIAR! HOW COULD THAT BE? BRING BACK MY SON OR I'LL TAKE YOU TO THE JUDGE.

LET'S GO. I'M NOT AFRAID!

SO THEY WENT TO THE JUDGE.

JUDGE, THIS ROGUE HAS KIDNAPPED MY ONLY SON. I WANT JUSTICE.

JWEERNADHANA, I COMMAND YOU TO RETURN HIS SON TO HIM.

JUDGE

MORAL : **TIT FOR TAT.**

THE JACKAL WHO FELL INTO A VAT OF INDIGO DYE.

ONCE A JACKAL GOT SO HUNGRY THAT HE VENTURED INTO A TOWN IN SEARCH OF FOOD.

THE TOWN DOGS ARE AFTER ME! HELP!

DYERS

TO SAVE HIMSELF FROM THE DOGS HE RAN INTO A DYER'S YARD AND...

... FELL INTO A VAT OF INDIGO DYE.

EYEO GLUB!

WHEN HE CAME OUT THE DOGS COULD NOT RECOGNISE HIM. THEY RAN AWAY IN PANIC.

I SHALL GO BACK TO THE JUNGLE.

BACK IN THE JUNGLE THE OTHER ANIMALS TOO WERE FRIGHTENED.

I MUST THINK FAST.

DON'T RUN AWAY. LORD BRAHMA HAS CROWNED ME YOUR NEW KING. COME BACK. I WILL PROTECT ALL OF YOU.

THUS ASSURED, THE ANIMALS RETURNED. THEN —

CHASE ALL THESE DIRTY JACKALS AWAY. I SHALL HAVE NOTHING TO DO WITH THEM.

THAT NIGHT WHEN THE JUNGLE WAS ABSOLUTELY STILL, THE JACKALS BEGAN HOWLING.

TRUE TO HIS NATURE THE BLUE JACKAL BEGAN HOWLING ALONG WITH HIS BROTHERS.

WOOOOO₀₀₀

WOOOOOO₀₀₀

HEY! OUR KING IS ONLY A JACKAL. WE HAVE BEEN FOOLED. HE SHALL DIE FOR THIS.

WOOO₀₀₀₀

SO THEY POUNCED ON THE BLUE JACKAL AND...

...THAT WAS THE END OF HIM.

MORAL: A COAT OF PAINT CANNOT HIDE ONE'S TRUE COLOURS.

THE HERON AND THE CRAB.

AN OLD HERON LIVED IN A JUNGLE NEAR A BIG LAKE WHICH WAS FULL OF FISHES, CRABS AND OTHER WATER CREATURES.

I AM SO OLD AND FEEBLE, I CAN HARDLY CATCH ANY FISH. UNLESS I FIND A WAY OUT, I WILL SOON DIE.

ONE DAY HE SAT AT THE EDGE OF THE LAKE AND BEGAN CRYING. A CRAB CAME TO HIM.

UNCLE, WHAT'S THE MATTER? WHY ARE YOU CRYING? AREN'T YOU GOING TO EAT ANY FISH TODAY?

FROM TODAY I SHALL FAST UNTO DEATH.

BUT WHY?

AN ASTROLOGER TOLD ME THIS MORNING THAT THERE WILL BE NO RAIN FOR 12 YEARS. THE LAKES WILL DRY UP. WE SHALL ALL DIE.

21

THE CRAB TOLD THIS TO ALL THE OTHER WATER CREATURES. THEY WERE PANIC-STRICKEN.

THEY SENT THE CRAB TO ASK THE HERON WHAT THEY SHOULD DO.

THIS MEANS SURE DEATH FOR US. PLEASE TELL US HOW WE CAN SAVE OURSELVES.

WELL, NOT FAR AWAY THERE IS A BIG LAKE, WHICH WILL NEVER DRY UP. I WILL TAKE YOU THERE, ONE BY ONE.

THE HERON HAD SUCCEEDED IN GAINING THEIR CONFIDENCE.

UNCLE! BROTHER! FATHER ME FIRST! NO ME! PLEASE!

THE WICKED HERON TOOK THEM, ONE BY ONE, TO A ROCK NEARBY AND ATE THEM.

THE MINUTE, THE HERON SAID THIS, THE CRAB CAUGHT HIS NECK BETWEEN HIS CLAWS AND STRANGLED HIM.

THAT WAS THE END OF THE WICKED OLD HERON.

BONG

THE CRAB GRIPPED THE HERON BY HIS NECK AND DRAGGED HIM SLOWLY TO THE LAKE.

HA! HA! HA! FASTING TO DEATH! POOR FISHES.

WHEN HE REACHED THE LAKE HE WAS STILL LAUGHING.

CRAB, WHY ARE YOU BACK? WHAT HAS HAPPENED TO UNCLE? WE ARE ALL WAITING FOR OUR TURN, TO BE TAKEN TO THE OTHER POND.

YOU FOOLS, HE HAS EATEN ALL YOUR BROTHERS. I FOUND OUT AND KILLED HIM.

MORAL: ONE MAY SMILE AND SMILE AND YET BE A VILLAIN.

DHARMABUDDHI AND PAPABUDDHI.

THE NEXT DAY PAPABUDDHI WENT TO DHARMABUDDHI'S HOUSE.

SO OFF THEY WENT. BUT WHEN THEY DUG UP THE PIT, THE POT OF MONEY WAS NOWHERE TO BE SEEN.

QUARRELLING ALL THE WAY, THEY WENT TO THE JUDGE.

I DIDN'T.

YOU DID.

THIS MAN HAS STOLEN THE MONEY. THE FOREST GOD IS MY WITNESS. HE WILL SPEAK THE TRUTH.

ALL RIGHT. WE WILL GO TO THE FOREST TOMORROW.

PAPABUDDHI WENT STRAIGHT HOME TO HIS FATHER.

FATHER, I HAVE STOLEN DHARMABUDDHI'S MONEY. YOU WILL HAVE TO DO AS I SAY IF I AM TO ESCAPE.

I'LL DO AS YOU WANT ME TO, MY SON.

THE NEXT MORNING DHARMABUDDHI, PAPABUDDHI, THE JUDGE AND THE VILLAGE ELDERS WENT UP TO WHERE THE MONEY HAD BEEN BURIED.

O TREE GOD. TELL US WHO THE THIEF IS!

DHARMABUDDHI IS THE THIEF.

WHILE THE OTHERS WERE BUSY DISCUSSING THE CASE, DHARMABUDDHI WAS BUSY COLLECTING DRIED LEAVES AND TWIGS. THESE HE PLACED NEAR THE HOLLOW OF THE TREE AND ---

... SET THEM ALIGHT.

AS THE FIRE ROSE INTO THE HOLLOW, OUT RAN PAPABUDDHI'S FATHER.

IT'S ALL MY SON'S FAULT.

PAPABUDDHI'S FATHER. WELL!

THE JUDGE UNDERSTOOD ALL AND WAS ANGRY.

PAPABUDDHI MADE ME DO THIS.

FOR THIS CRIME HE SHALL BE HANGED ON THIS VERY TREE RIGHT NOW.

MORAL : HONESTY IS THE BEST POLICY.

THE LION AND THE HARE.

IN A CERTAIN JUNGLE THERE LIVED A LION CALLED BHASURAKA. HE WAS VERY STRONG AND KILLED THE ANIMALS IN THE JUNGLE JUST FOR FUN.

GRRRR

OH! WHY DOES HE HAVE TO KILL US WHEN HE IS NOT HUNGRY?

ONE DAY ALL THE SURVIVING ANIMALS APPROACHED BHASURAKA.

MASTER, WHY KILL US ALL WHEN ONE OF US WOULD SATISFY YOUR HUNGER? FROM TODAY ONE OF US WILL COME TO YOU EACH DAY. IN RETURN YOU MUST LET THE OTHERS LIVE IN PEACE.

ALL RIGHT. BUT IF YOU FAIL TO COME, I SHALL KILL ALL OF YOU.

EVERY DAY THE ANIMALS DREW LOTS. ONE DAY —

OH! POOR HARE!
IT IS YOUR TURN TODAY.

MOST RELUCTANTLY THE HARE MADE HIS WAY TO BHASURAKA.

I WISH I COULD KILL HIM AND SAVE MY LIFE!

SUDDENLY HE CAME ACROSS A WELL. HE WAS JUBILANT.

NOW I KNOW A WAY TO KILL HIM. AND I WON'T FAIL.

BY THE TIME THE HARE REACHED BHASURAKA IT WAS SUNSET. AND BHASU-RAKA WAS FURIOUS.

THE FIRST THING I'LL DO TOMOR-ROW IS TO KILL ALL THE ANIMALS.

CAUTIOUSLY THE HARE NEARED BHASURAKA.

AS IT IS YOU ARE SMALL. APART FROM THAT, YOU ARE LATE. I'LL KILL YOU NOW AND THE OTHERS TOMORROW.

MORAL : NOTHING IS IMPOSSIBLE FOR A CLEVER MAN.

THE BRAHMIN AND THE GOAT

TALES FROM THE PANCHATANTRA

The route to your roots

THE BRAHMIN AND
THE GOAT

A collection of tales compiled by Vishnu Sharma, for his young students some 2,200 years ago, the Panchatantra is still correcting common human weaknesses with its wry humour.

Script	Illustrations	Editor
Shyamala Kutty	Ashok Dongre	Anant Pai

THE BRAHMAN AND THE GOAT

ONE DAY, A BRAHMAN CALLED MITRA SHARMA WAS RETURNING HOME FROM A NEIGHBOURING VILLAGE.

IT WAS KIND OF THAT VILLAGER TO GIVE ME THIS PLUMP GOAT FOR THE SACRIFICE.

JUST THEN, THREE HUNGRY CROOKS HAPPENED TO SEE HIM.

WHAT A PLUMP GOAT!

IT WOULD MAKE A FINE DINNER! LET'S TRICK HIM OUT OF IT.

1

WHAT'S THE MATTER? AM I MAD OR ARE THEY?

HARDLY HAD HE WALKED A FEW YARDS AHEAD WHEN—

O BRAHMAN, DROP THE DONKEY BEFORE ANYONE SEES YOU! PEOPLE WILL TALK.

NO! THREE OF THEM CANNOT BE WRONG!

THE BRAHMAN DID NOT UTTER A WORD. HE PULLED THE GOAT OFF HIS SHOULDERS, FLUNG IT TO THE GROUND...

MORAL: TRUST YOURSELF BEFORE YOU TRUST OTHERS.

THE KING ELEPHANT AND THE MICE

ONE HOT SUMMER, ALL THE RIVERS IN A FOREST RAN DRY.

THE KING ELEPHANT OF A HERD OF ELEPHANTS WAS WORRIED.

IF I DON'T FIND SOME WATER SOON, WE WILL ALL DIE.

SUDDENLY, ONE OF HIS RETINUE LUMBERED UP TO HIM.

WATER! I KNOW WHERE WE CAN GET WATER. A BIRD TOLD ME THAT IN A LAKE NOT FAR FROM HERE, THERE IS ENOUGH WATER FOR TEN HERDS LIKE OURS!

THE KING WAS RELIEVED. HE GAVE ORDERS AND THE MARCH BEGAN.

YOU LEAD US, WE WILL FOLLOW.

TOWARDS NOON, THE ELEPHANTS SPOTTED THE LAKE.

LOOK! THERE IT.IS!

AND THEY CHARGED TOWARDS THE WATER, TRAMPLING EVERYTHING IN THEIR WAKE.

RUN! RUN FOR YOUR LIVES!

ELEPHANTS! IT'S A STAMPEDE!

AMONG THE VICTIMS WERE A NUMBER OF MICE WHO HAD BURROWED A COLONY NEAR THE LAKE. LATER, THE MICE THAT HAD MANAGED TO ESCAPE, HELD A MEETING.

ONE OF THEM HAD AN IDEA.

WHY DON'T WE GO TO THE KING OF THE HERD AND RE-QUEST HIM NOT TO COME THIS WAY AGAIN?

AN EXCELLENT IDEA!

SO THEY WENT TO THE KING ELEPHANT.

O KING, WE HAVE BEEN LIVING NEAR THIS LAKE FOR GENERATIONS. WHILE YOUR HERD CAME CHARGING THIS WAY, IT TRAMPLED TO DEATH NEARLY HALF OUR CLAN. WE BEG OF YOU...

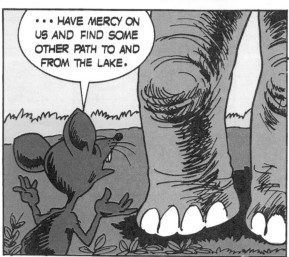

... HAVE MERCY ON US AND FIND SOME OTHER PATH TO AND FROM THE LAKE.

SPARE OUR LIVES. SMALL THOUGH WE ARE, SOME DAY WE MAY PROVE USEFUL TO YOU.

PAH! HOW CAN THESE TEENY-WEENY MICE BE USEFUL TO US?

BUT THE ELEPHANT WAS KIND-HEARTED.

SET YOUR MINDS AT REST. I SHALL TELL MY HERD TO TAKE ANOTHER PATH.

O KING, WE ARE GRATEFUL TO YOU. IF EVER YOU NEED US, WE SHALL BE WITH YOU.

AS HE WATCHED THE GRATEFUL, HAPPY MICE SCAMPER AWAY, LITTLE DID THE KING ELEPHANT REALISE HOW SOON HE WOULD NEED THEM!

A FEW DAYS LATER, AS THE ELEPHANTS LUMBERED TOWARDS THE LAKE AS USUAL—

CHEEEE

IT'S A TRAP!

TAKE CARE!

TRAPPERS ON OUR TRAIL!

THREE DAYS LATER, THE TRAPPERS CAME.

9

I WONDER HOW AND WITH WHOSE HELP WE WILL BE FREED; BUT FREE OUR- SELVES WE WILL.

SUDDENLY, HE REMEMBERED THE MICE.

MY FRIENDS THE MICE! WHY DIDN'T I THINK OF THEM EARLIER! BUT HOW SHALL I SEND A MESSAGE TO THEM?

THAT NIGHT, WHEN ONE OF THE ELEPHANTS WHO HAD ESCAPED CAME TO SEE THE KING —

GO TO THE MICE AND TELL THEM OF OUR PLIGHT.

AS SOON AS THE MICE HEARD THE ELEPHANT'S STORY —

WE WILL COME RIGHT AWAY. LEAD US TO THEM.

THE BRAHMAN, THE THIEF AND THE RAKSHASA

ONCE THERE WAS A BRAHMAN NAMED DRONA, WHO HAD GIVEN UP ALL THE LUXURIES OF LIFE.

ONE DAY, A DEVOTEE CAME TO SEE HIM.

MASTER, YOU ARE LEAN AND HUNGRY. PLEASE ACCEPT THESE.

TWO CALVES! MAY YOU EVER BE PROSPEROUS.

THE BRAHMAN FED THE CALVES ON BUTTER, OIL AND GRAIN. A THIEF NOTICED ALL THIS.

WHAT FAT CALVES! THIS VERY NIGHT, I SHALL STEAL THEM.

13

THE FRIGHTENED BRAHMAN INVOKED HIS DEITY.

O LORD, PLEASE DRIVE AWAY THE RAKSHASA.

IN AN INSTANT, THE RAKSHASA VANISHED.

AS FOR YOU, RUN OFF OR I'LL BEAT YOU UP!

THE THIEF IS GONE. THE CALVES ARE SAFE, AND I AM ALIVE! THANK GOD!

MORAL: WHEN YOUR ENEMIES QUARREL AMONGST THEMSELVES, YOU STAND TO GAIN.

THE LION, THE JACKAL AND THE CAVE

ONCE A LION CALLED KHARANAKHARA COULD NOT FIND ANYTHING TO EAT. HE WAS VERY HUNGRY.

ANOTHER DAY OF STARVATION! I CAN'T BEAR IT ANY MORE.

AT SUNSET, HE REACHED A BIG CAVE.

SOME ANIMAL MUST BE LIVING IN THIS CAVE. I'LL GO IN AND AWAIT ITS RETURN.

AS THE LION WAITED INSIDE THE CAVE, A JACKAL ARRIVED.

STRANGE! A LION'S FOOTPRINTS, LEADING INTO MY CAVE BUT NONE COMING OUT.

19

THE MOUSE AND THE SAGE

LONG, LONG AGO, IN A HERMITAGE ON THE BANK OF THE RIVER GANGA, THERE LIVED A SAGE CALLED YAJNAVALKYA.

ONE DAY AS YAJNAVALKYA WAS SAYING HIS PRAYERS IN THE SACRED STREAM—

WHAT'S THIS! A MOUSE!

FOR A MOMENT, THE SAGE WONDERED WHAT TO DO WITH IT.

IF I LEAVE IT ON THE BANK, THE HAWK MAY ONCE AGAIN POUNCE ON IT.

THEN AN IDEA STRUCK HIM.

WHY NOT! AND MY WIFE HAS ALWAYS WANTED A DAUGHTER. YES. I'LL TURN IT INTO A BABY GIRL.

SO, USING HIS YOGIC POWERS, HE CHANGED THE MOUSE INTO A BABY GIRL AND TOOK HER HOME TO HIS WIFE.

TAKE HER, DEAR WIFE, AND REAR HER AS OUR OWN DAUGHTER.

AH! MY PRAYERS HAVE AT LAST BEEN ANSWERED.

THE GIRL GREW UP IN THE SAGE'S HOUSE. SOON SHE WAS TWELVE YEARS OLD.

DEAR HUSBAND, DON'T YOU THINK IT'S TIME WE FOUND A SUITABLE HUSBAND FOR OUR DAUGHTER?

YOU ARE RIGHT. I MUST GIVE HER TO SOMEONE REALLY WORTHY OF HER.

I WILL SUMMON THE SUN AND GIVE HER TO HIM.

A GOOD CHOICE.

AND YAJNAVALKYA SUMMONED HIM.

HOLY SIR, WHAT DO YOU WANT OF ME?

I WANT YOU TO MARRY MY DAUGHTER, IF SHE IS WILLING.

THEN THE SAGE TURNED TO HIS DAUGHTER.

WILL YOU MARRY THE SUN WHO GIVES LIGHT AND WARMTH TO ALL THE THREE WORLDS?

NO, FATHER. I DO NOT LIKE HIM BECAUSE HE IS TOO HOT. ISN'T THERE SOMEONE GREATER THAN HIM?

O BLESSED ONE, IS THERE ANYONE SUPERIOR TO YOU?

YES. THE CLOUD. HE CAN BLOT ME OUT WHENEVER HE FEELS LIKE IT.

SO THE SAGE SUMMONED THE CLOUD.

LITTLE GIRL, WILL YOU MARRY HIM?

NO, FATHER. HE IS DARK AND COLD. PLEASE FIND ME SOMEONE BETTER.

I SHALL MARRY YOU TO HIM, MY DAUGHTER. WHO COULD BE STEADIER THAN HIM?

BUT TO HIS SURPRISE, HIS DAUGHTER WAS ALMOST IN TEARS.

O FATHER, PLEASE SPARE ME. HE IS SO COARSE AND LIFELESS. PLEASE, PLEASE FIND SOMEONE MORE LIVELY.

THE SAGE LOOKED UP AT THE WISE MOUNTAIN.

O MIGHTY, WISE ONE, CAN YOU SUGGEST SOMEONE MORE SUITABLE?

OF COURSE, I CAN. THE BEST MATE FOR YOUR DAUGHTER WOULD BE THE KING OF THE MICE. HE'S THE LIVELIEST, FRISKIEST CREATURE I'VE SEEN IN MY LIFETIME. AND I AM MANY HUNDRED YEARS OLD.

SO THE SAGE SUMMONED THE KING OF THE MICE. AS SOON AS HE APPEARED THE LITTLE GIRL QUIVERED WITH JOY.

FATHER, HE'S THE ONE I'LL MARRY. PLEASE TURN ME INTO A MOUSE SO THAT I CAN KEEP HOUSE FOR HIM AS A GOOD WIFE SHOULD.

THE SAGE USED HIS YOGIC POWERS AND TURNED HER BACK INTO A MOUSE.

HE THEN GAVE HER IN MARRIAGE TO THE KING OF THE MICE.

STRANGE ARE THE WAYS OF NATURE. I BROUGHT HER UP AS A HUMAN CHILD. I OFFERED HER THE SUN, THE CLOUD, THE WIND, THE MOUNTAIN; AND YET, SHE FOUND SHE COULD BE HAPPY ONLY WITH THE HUMBLE MOUSE.

MORAL: LET A MOUSE BE A MOUSE.

THE BIRD WHO SHED GOLDEN DROPPINGS

IN A HUGE TREE, THERE ONCE LIVED A BIRD CALLED SINDHUKA. ONE DAY, A HUNTER WHO HAD COME THERE TO CATCH BIRDS SAT DOWN TO REST UNDER THE TREE.

SUDDENLY —

CHEE! CHEE! A BIRD'S DROPPINGS!

AS HE BENT DOWN TO BRUSH OFF THE DROPPINGS —

WHAT! IT'S TURNED INTO GOLD!

NEVER HAVE I SEEN THIS KIND OF THING BEFORE. I MUST CATCH THAT BIRD.

JUST THEN THE BIRD FLEW AWAY.

AH! THAT MUST BE THE BRANCH WHERE IT USUALLY SITS. I'LL SET A TRAP RIGHT WHERE IT WAS PERCHING.

SO HE SET THE TRAP AND WAITED.

THAT EVENING, WHEN THE BIRD RETURNED HOME TO ROOST, IT DID NOT EXAMINE ITS PERCH FOR ANY LURKING DANGER AS A GOOD BIRD SHOULD.

THE NEXT MOMENT, THE NET HAD FALLEN OVER IT.

THE HUNTER PUT THE BIRD INTO A CAGE.

I'LL TAKE HIM HOME. I'LL NEVER HAVE TO HUNT AGAIN.

ON THE WAY HOME, HOWEVER, HE HAD SECOND THOUGHTS.

SUPPOSING SOME-ONE SEES IT AND TELLS THE KING.

THE KING WOULD BE ANGRY WITH ME FOR NOT TELLING HIM ABOUT IT.

29

THE MINISTERS, HOW-EVER, DID NOT QUITE LIKE A MERE BIRD GETTING SO MUCH ATTENTION.

O KING, IT IS NOT WISE TO TRUST THE WORDS OF A MERE HUNTER. HOW CAN A BIRD'S DROP-PINGS TURN INTO GOLD?

BLINDED BY JEALOUSY, THEY GAVE THE KING FOOLISH COUNSEL.

IT IS CRUEL TO CAGE THIS POOR BIRD BECAUSE OF WHAT THAT HUNTER SAYS. BIRDS SHOULD BE FLYING FREELY IN THE FOREST.

HOW RIGHT THEY ARE!

THE FOOLISH KING TRUSTED THE MINISTER'S WORDS WITHOUT FINDING OUT THE FACTS FOR HIMSELF.

ALL RIGHT, THEN SET IT FREE.

AN ATTENDANT OPENED THE CAGE.

THE DELIGHTED BIRD FLEW TO THE TOP OF THE TALL PALACE GATES...

...AND PERCHING HIMSELF THERE, LET FALL HIS DROPPINGS.

WHY! THE DROPPINGS HAVE, INDEED, TURNED TO GOLD! FOOLS THAT WE ARE! QUICK! GET THE BIRD.

BUT THE BIRD FLEW AWAY.

NOT AGAIN, MY KING. WE HAVE ALL BEEN A PACK OF FOOLS; FIRST I, THEN THE HUNTER, THEN YOUR MINISTERS AND THEN YOU. NO, I'LL NOT BE SO FOOLISH AS TO BE CAUGHT AGAIN.

MORAL: ASCERTAIN A FACT BEFORE YOU ACCEPT ANOTHER'S WORD FOR IT.

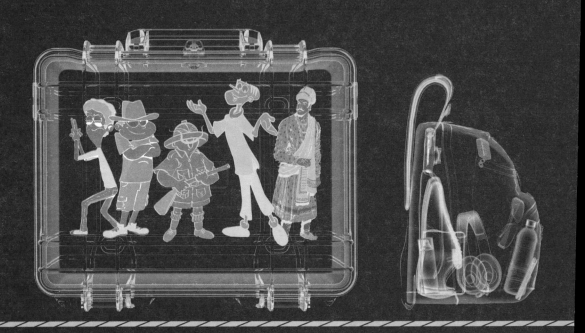

CROWS AND OWLS

TALES FROM THE PANCHATANTRA

The route to your roots

CROWS AND OWLS

Pandit Vishnu Sharma found an ideal teaching tool – tales from a collection he called the Panchatantra. Gently guiding his pupils towards a life of honour and nobility, his fables provided joyful entertainment as well. They are read even today, 2,000 years later, by peoples of diverse cultures in various languages. All that is foolish as well as unkind in the human character is starkly revealed, together with some useful advice: pick your friends wisely!

Script
Luis Fernandes

Illustrations
M. Mohandas

Editor
Anant Pai

Cover Illustration By: C.M. Vitankar

CROWS AND OWLS

A COLONY OF CROWS DWELT IN A GREAT BANYAN TREE IN A FOREST. THE NAME OF THEIR KING WAS CLOUDY.

THE CROWS WERE CONSTANTLY HARASSED BY THEIR POWERFUL ENEMIES, THE OWLS. THEIR KING, FOE-CRUSHER WOULD ATTACK ANY CROW HE CAME ACROSS.

WHOOO-OOOO-IT!

THEN ONE DAY, CLOUDY CALLED A MEETING OF HIS FIVE COUNSELLORS.

THE OWLS ARE BECOMING A MENACE.

THEY ARE ARROGANT AND POWERFUL AND THEY ATTACK US AT NIGHT WHEN WE CANNOT SEE. WE CANNOT COUNTER-ATTACK DURING THE DAY BECAUSE WE DON'T KNOW WHERE THEY DWELL.

ADVISE ME, COUNSELLORS. WHAT SHOULD WE DO?

3

THE OWL LOST NO TIME IN REPORTING WHAT HE HAD HEARD AND SEEN TO HIS MASTER, KING FOE-CRUSHER.

YOUR MAJESTY, THE CROWS ARE FIGHTING AMONGST THEMSELVES.

THEY HAVE THROWN OUT ONE OF THEIR MINISTERS.

THEN THIS IS A GOOD TIME TO ATTACK THEM. A DISORGANISED ENEMY IS EASILY DEFEATED.

FOLLOW ME, MY FRIENDS.

FOE-CRUSHER AND HIS OWLS ATTACKED THE BANYAN TREE WITH BLOODCURDLING WAR CRIES.

WHOOOO!

WHOOO-IEEEE!

BUT THEY SOON REALISED THAT THERE WAS NOT A SINGLE CROW IN THE TREE.

THE COWARDS HAVE FLED!

OLD LIVE-STRONG WHO HAD BEEN WATCHING THE PROCEEDINGS FROM THE GROUND WAS PLEASED WITH THE WAY THINGS WERE GOING.

THE FIRST PART OF MY PLAN HAS SUCCEEDED.

NEXT COMES THE MOST DANGEROUS PART... BUT THERE'S NO TURNING BACK NOW.

WELL, HERE GOES.

CAW! CAW!

LOOK, A CROW!

THE OWL SOON RETURNED WITH FOE-CRUSHER WHO WAS ASTONISHED TO SEE THE BATTERED CONDITION OF THE OLD CROW.

FOE-CRUSHER HAD FIVE ANCESTRAL COUNSELLORS. THEIR NAMES WERE RED-EYE, FIERCE-EYE, HOOK-NOSE, FLAME-EYE AND WALL-EAR.

THE CROW SEEKS ASYLUM. WHAT IS YOUR OPINION, RED-EYE?

SLAY HIM WITHOUT FURTHER DELAY, MY LORD. HE IS A CROW!

BUT THE OTHER COUNSELLORS WERE MORE CHARITABLE.

GRANT HIM REFUGE, O KING!

IT WOULD BE WRONG TO KILL ONE WHO SEEKS YOUR PROTECTION.

HE MAY PROVE USEFUL TO US IN OUR WAR WITH THE CROWS.

DO NOT LISTEN TO THEM, YOUR MAJESTY. SLAY HIM! HE IS UP TO NO GOOD!

I HAVE ALREADY MADE UP MY MIND, RED-EYE. THE CROW STAYS WITH US. WE SHALL TAKE HIM TO OUR FORTRESS.

THE OWLS LIFTED UP LIVE-STRONG AND CARRIED HIM TO THEIR FORTRESS.

I HAVE FOOLED THEM ALL EXCEPT THE SHREWD RED-EYE. HE HAS GUESSED MY TRUE PURPOSE.

THIS IS OUR FORTRESS, SIR. HERE YOU MAY STAY IN COMFORT AND HONOUR.

HO, THERE! MAKE OUR GUEST COMFORTABLE. LOOK AFTER HIS NEEDS.

IF I STAY IN THEIR MIDST IT WILL BE DIFFICULT FOR ME TO GO ABOUT MY BUSINESS WITHOUT BEING OBSERVED.

O KING, IT WOULD NOT BE PROPER FOR ME TO ENTER YOUR FORTRESS. I AM, AFTER ALL, A CROW AND UNWORTHY OF THE HONOUR.

9

11

EACH DAY THEREAFTER, LIVE-STRONG WENT INTO THE FOREST AND RETURNED WITH A TWIG WHICH HE DROPPED INSIDE THE GATE.

I AM BUILDING A NEST, YOUR MAJESTY. I HOPE YOU DO NOT MIND.

OF COURSE, NOT!

LET US KNOW IF YOU NEED ANY HELP.

SOON THERE WAS A LARGE PILE OF TWIGS AT THE GATE, BUT NONE OF THE OWLS STOPPED TO WONDER WHY THEIR GUEST REQUIRED SO BIG A NEST.

THEN ONE MORNING WHEN THE OWLS WERE ASLEEP, LIVE-STRONG QUIETLY LEFT THE FORTRESS.

HE FLEW DIRECTLY TO A NEARBY MOUNTAIN WHERE CLOUDY AND THE OTHER CROWS WERE WAITING FOR HIM.

WE ARE DELIGHTED TO SEE YOU BACK WITH US!

AND SOON—

FIRE! THE CAVE IS ON FIRE!

THE OWLS, STILL HALF ASLEEP, TRIED TO RUSH OUT OF THE CAVE BUT WERE BEATEN BACK BY THE FLAMES.

THE CROW HAS DONE THIS! I SHOULD HAVE LISTENED TO MY FAITHFUL RED-EYE!

WE ARE DOOMED! DOOMED!

AH!

THE CAVE, CLOSED AS IT WAS FROM ALL SIDES, BECAME A FIERY FURNACE.

THOSE OF THE OWLS WHO MANAGED TO EVADE THE FLAMES WERE SUFFOCATED BY THE FUMES. ALL OF THEM, INCLUDING KING FOE-CRUSHER, PERISHED.

AND THUS DID THE CROWS RID THEMSELVES OF THEIR POWERFUL BUT DIM-WITTED ENEMIES, THE OWLS.

THE NOBLE ENEMY

A MAN WAS SEARCHING FOR GEMS ON THE TOP OF A CERTAIN MOUNTAIN.

AFTER A LONG UNSUCCESSFUL SEARCH, HE WAS EXHAUSTED AND THREW HIMSELF ON THE GROUND BEHIND A ROCK.

I'LL TAKE A SHORT NAP AND THEN TRY AGAIN.

BZZ...BZZ...BZZ...

...TOO MANY DACOITS AROUND HERE...

...THE GEMS...

GOOD GOD! THOSE YOUNG MEN HAVE FOUND SOME GEMS!

SEARCH THEM!

THE MEN SEARCHED THEIR CAPTIVES THOROUGHLY.

THERE HAS BEEN SOME MISTAKE. WE DON'T HAVE ANY GEMS WITH US!

WE CAN'T FIND ANYTHING ON THEM, CHIEF.

HOW'S THAT!

OH, WELL! THE BIRD MUST HAVE BEEN MISTAKEN.

ALL RIGHT. LET THEM GO.

BUT AS SOON AS THEY LEFT, THE BIRD BEGAN TO SING THE SAME SONG AGAIN.

THEY HAVE GEMS WITH THEM... THEY HAVE GEMS WITH THEM...

WHAT! HAVE THEY DECEIVED ME, THEN?

GO AFTER THEM! BRING THEM BACK!

THE FOUR MEN WERE BROUGHT BACK AND SEARCHED AGAIN.

NO! NOTHING ON THEM.

HOW CAN THAT BE? MY BIRD INSISTS...

AHA!

THE GEMS MUST BE IN YOUR STOMACHS! YOU HAVE SWALLOWED THEM!

ULP! WE ARE DONE FOR!

TAKE THEM AWAY AND CUT OPEN THEIR BELLIES.

NO, NO!

I AM BEYOND HELP. WHEN THEY FIND GEMS IN THEIR STOMACHS THEY WILL CUT OPEN MINE TOO.

ON THE OTHER HAND, THEY MAY CUT ME FIRST. EITHER WAY I AM DOOMED.

BUT I COULD SAVE THE OTHER FELLOWS. LET ME TRY...

YOU WON'T FIND ANY GEMS IN OUR STOMACHS, SIR. BUT IF YOU INSIST ON SEEING FOR YOURSELF LET ME BE THE FIRST TO DIE.

IT WOULD BE UNBEARABLE FOR ME TO WATCH THE STOMACHS OF MY FRIENDS BEING CUT OPEN.

WHETHER YOU DIE FIRST OR LAST MAKES NO DIFFERENCE TO ME.

TAKE HIM AWAY AND GRANT HIM HIS WISH.

THANK YOU.

IF MY LITTLE TRICK WORKS, MY DEATH WILL NOT HAVE BEEN IN VAIN.

THE MAN WAS TAKEN AWAY. LATER—

THERE WASN'T A SINGLE GEM IN HIS STOMACH.

WHAT!

SO MY BIRD CAN MAKE A MISTAKE AFTER ALL.

THERE WERE NO GEMS IN HIS STOMACH. THERE WON'T BE ANY IN THE STOMACHS OF HIS FRIENDS EITHER.

THERE HAS BEEN A TERRIBLE MISTAKE, MY FRIENDS. I AM SORRY THAT YOUR COMRADE IS DEAD.

YOU MAY GO.

LITTLE DID THE CHIEF REALISE THAT HE HAD DONE EXACTLY WHAT THE DEAD MAN HAD HOPED HE WOULD DO.

THE FRIENDS TOO, UNAWARE THAT THEY HAD BEEN SAVED BY A CLEVER RUSE, THOUGHT THEY HAD JUST BEEN VERY LUCKY, AND LOST NO TIME IN GETTING OUT OF THE VILLAGE.

MORAL: A SENSIBLE ENEMY CAN OFTEN PROVE TO BE YOUR BEST FRIEND.

THE BIRD AND THE MONKEYS

ONE CHILLY WINTER EVENING—

BRRR—RRR... IT'S COLD.

LOOK, BROTHER! A SPARK OF FIRE.

IT WAS A GLOW-WORM GOING PAST.

I'VE GOT IT!

PUT IT UNDER THIS PILE OF LEAVES.

WE WILL SOON HAVE A BIG BLAZING FIRE TO KEEP OURSELVES WARM.

YOU ARE MAKING A MISTAKE, GOOD SIRS.

THAT'S A FIREFLY YOU'VE CAUGHT...

...NOT A SPARK OF FIRE.

IGNORE HER!

LET'S BLOW ON THE LEAVES. THEY'LL CATCH FIRE FASTER THAT WAY.

MORAL: DON'T TRY TO TEACH THOSE WHO CANNOT BE TAUGHT.

THE CAMEL WHO WAS BEGUILED BY HIS COMPANIONS

A MERCHANT WAS LEADING A CARAVAN OF HEAVILY-LADEN CAMELS THROUGH A JUNGLE...

...WHEN ONE OF THEM, OVERCOME BY FATIGUE, COLLAPSED.

LET US SHIFT HIS LOAD ONTO THE OTHERS AND BE OFF. WE MUST NOT LET THIS LAZY CREATURE DELAY US.

LATER, WHEN THE CAMEL RECOVERED HIS STRENGTH—

THEY HAVE GONE! AND I AM ALONE IN THIS STRANGE JUNGLE.

FORTUNATELY, THERE'S PLENTY OF GRASS HERE. AT LEAST I WON'T STARVE.

DAYS PASSED AND THE CAMEL SOMEHOW SURVIVED THE PERILS OF THE JUNGLE.

THEN ONE DAY, A LION FOLLOWED BY A LEOPARD, A JACKAL AND A CROW, CAME BY.

25

THEY LOOK SO SAD. THEY MUST BE WORRYING ABOUT MY HEALTH. I WISH I COULD FEED THEM AS ALWAYS.

I AM SORRY I CANNOT PROVIDE YOU WITH FOOD NOW, MY FRIENDS. I AM TOO WEAK TO HUNT.

YOU WILL HAVE TO FEND FOR YOURSELVES TILL I RECOVER.

WHAT ARE YOU SAYING, MASTER?

HOW COULD WE EVEN THINK OF EATING WHEN YOU ARE STARVING!

THE LION WAS PLEASED WITH THE JACKAL'S REPLY.

YOU HAVE SHOWN YOURSELVES TO BE LOYAL SERVANTS. GO AND ROUND UP AN ANIMAL AND DRIVE IT THIS WAY SO THAT I MAY KILL IT FOR FOOD.

THE JACKAL AND HIS FRIENDS SCOURED THE JUNGLE BUT COULD NOT FIND ANY ANIMAL.

FINALLY, THEY FOUND THEMSELVES BACK WHERE THEY HAD STARTED.

THERE'S REALLY... ...NO NEED... TO EXERT OURSELVES LIKE THIS.

WHAT ELSE CAN WE DO?

WELL, THERE'S THE CAMEL. HIS FLESH COULD SUSTAIN US ALL FOR SEVERAL DAYS.

FORGET IT. THE KING WILL NEVER HURT ANY ANIMAL THAT IS UNDER HIS PROTECTION.

I'LL HAVE A WORD WITH HIM IN ANY CASE.

O KING, WE COULD NOT FIND AN ANIMAL FOR YOU. BUT THERE'S NO NEED FOR YOU TO STARVE.

YOU CAN EAT THE CAMEL.

WHAT!

ARE YOU SUGGESTING THAT I HURT AN ANIMAL THAT IS UNDER MY PROTECTION?

GET OUT OF MY SIGHT, YOU WRETCH!

PLEASE DON'T MISUNDERSTAND ME, O KING.

I WAS ONLY THINKING OF YOUR WELFARE. OUR OWN LIVES ARE WORTHLESS WHEN YOURS IS AT STAKE.

I KNOW IT WOULD BE WRONG FOR YOU TO HURT THE CAMEL IN ORDINARY CIRCUMSTANCES.

BUT WHAT IF HE HIMSELF DEVOTEDLY OFFERED HIS FLESH TO YOU? THEN NO ONE COULD BLAME YOU FOR SLAYING HIM.

I SUPPOSE YOU ARE RIGHT.

IF THE CAMEL WERE TO MAKE SUCH AN OFFER I MIGHT ACCEPT IT.

THE WILY JACKAL RAN BACK TO HIS FRIENDS WHO HAD NOW BEEN JOINED BY THE CAMEL.

FRIENDS, OUR KING IS DYING OF STARVATION. LET US GO AND BEG HIM TO EAT ONE OF US.

IT IS THE LEAST WE CAN DO FOR SUCH A NOBLE SOUL.

WHAT IS IT, MY FRIENDS? HAVE YOU CAUGHT ANY CREATURE?

NO, O KING. WE WERE NOT ABLE TO CATCH ANY CREATURE. YOU MAY EAT ANY ONE OF US INSTEAD.

AND THAT ONE WILL BE THE CAMEL!

I HOPE BROTHER LEOPARD TOO, CATCHES ON!

EAT ME, MASTER AND PROLONG YOUR LIFE FOR A DAY.

NO, NO, YOU'RE TOO SMALL. THE MASTER'S HUNGER WOULD HARDLY BE APPEASED BY EATING YOU.

EAT ME, MASTER.

AS IF YOU'RE VERY BIG YOURSELF.

IT IS ME YOU SHOULD EAT, MASTER.

ALL OF THEM HAVE OFFERED TO LAY DOWN THEIR LIVES FOR THE KING, BUT HE HAS NOT HURT ANY OF THEM.

NOW LET ME TOO MAKE A NOBLE GESTURE. THEY'LL PROTECT ME TOO!

SO THE POOR CAMEL STEPPED FORWARD.

STAND ASIDE, FRIEND LEOPARD. HOW CAN THE MASTER EAT YOU? YOU AND HE BELONG TO THE SAME FAMILY — WELL ALMOST.

EAT ME, MASTER.

AN OMINOUS SILENCE GREETED THE CAMEL'S OFFER. THEN—

I ACCEPT YOUR OFFER, O NOBLE CAMEL.

WHA...?!

BEFORE THE CAMEL COULD GET OVER HIS SHOCK, THE THREE ANIMALS RUSHED AT HIM...

...AND KILLED HIM. THUS DID THREE ROGUES TAKE ADVANTAGE OF THE TRUST REPOSED IN THEM BY A COMRADE.

MORAL: WATCH YOUR STEP WITH FALSE FRIENDS.

BEGINNING OF AN EPIC SAGA
BALA KAND

The divine story of
Rama's birth

His heroic adventur
with Lakshmana

The stirring legend
of Shiva's bow

Amar Chitra Kat
presents the sev
kands of Valmik
Ramayana.

Start your
collection
now!

HOW THE JACKAL ATE THE ELEPHANT

TALES FROM THE PANCHATANTRA

The route to your roots

HOW THE JACKAL ATE THE ELEPHANT

In Vishnu Sharma's famous Panchatantra tales, animals talk and act like humans. A wily jackal or a deceiving donkey, an impetuous frog-king or an arrogant lion often mirror our everyday world. Through these tales the master storyteller reveals the secret of living life wisely yet happily to generations of readers all over the world.

Script	Illustrations	Editor
Kamala Chandrakant	Ram Waeerkar	Anant Pai

HOW THE JACKAL ATE THE ELEPHANT

MAHACHATURAKA, THE JACKAL WAS VERY HAPPY. HE HAD FOUND A DEAD ELEPHANT. ENOUGH FOOD FOR WEEKS!

BUT I'M GOING TO NEED HELP TO CUT INTO HIS HIDE AND REACH THE FLESH.

AT THAT MOMENT, A LION HAPPENED TO COME BY.

I'D BETTER OFFER HIM THE ELEPHANT AND WIN HIS FAVOUR.

1

4

COME ON. BE BOLD AND EAT. I'LL KEEP WATCH AND WARN YOU, IF I SEE HIM COMING.

THE LEOPARD NEEDED NO MORE COAXING. HE BEGAN TO TEAR AWAY AT THE ELEPHANT'S HIDE.

AS SOON AS THE HIDE WAS CUT THROUGH —

HERE COMES THE LION. QUICK! RUN OFF!

THE LEOPARD DID NOT EVEN STOP TO LOOK UP. TURNING ON HIS HEELS, HE RAN FOR HIS LIFE.

THE JACKAL WAS ABOUT TO FEED ON THE FLESH WHEN ANOTHER JACKAL CAME BY.

OH! THIS ONE IS MY EQUAL. I'LL FIGHT HIM OFF.

BARING HIS FANGS HE CHARGED...

...AND CHASED AWAY THE UNWELCOME GUEST.

ALL THIS MEAT! ALL FOR MYSELF! I NEED NOT LOOK FOR FOOD FOR WEEKS.

MORAL: MIGHTY BRAWN IS NO MATCH AGAINST NIMBLE BRAIN.

THE FROG KING AND THE SNAKE

GANGADATTA WAS THE KING OF THE FROGS WHO LIVED IN A WELL. HE COULD NOT GET ALONG WITH SOME OF HIS RELATIVES BECAUSE THEY OFTEN TREATED HIM BADLY.

ONE DAY HE TURNED TO HIS WIFE —

HOW DARE THEY TREAT ME, THEIR KING, IN THIS WAY! I MUST TEACH THEM A LESSON.

TAKE CARE, DEAR HUSBAND, THAT IN TRYING TO HARM THEM YOU DON'T GET US INTO TROUBLE.

BUT, IGNORING HER ADVICE, HE LEAPT FROM PAIL ...

...TO PAIL, UP THE WATER-WHEEL ...

... AND CAME OUT OF THE WELL. JUST THEN HE SAW PRIYADARSHANA, THE SNAKE, SLIDE INTO HIS HOLE.

AH! I'LL ASK HIM TO BE MY GUEST AND EAT MY WICKED RELATIVES.

HEY, PRIYA-DARSHANA! COME OUT.

THAT'S NO SNAKE CALLING ME. AND I DON'T HAVE ANY FRIENDS APART FROM SNAKES. PERHAPS IT'S A SNAKE CHARMER!

COME OUT, PRIYADARSHANA. I AM GANGADATTA, THE FROG-KING. I WANT TO MAKE FRIENDS WITH YOU.

IMPOSSIBLE! CAN HAY EVER MAKE FRIENDS WITH FIRE? WHAT YOU SAY MAKES NO SENSE.

I AGREE THAT WE ARE BORN ENEMIES. NEVERTHE-LESS, I NEED YOUR HELP. I WANT YOU TO EAT MY ENEMIES.

WHO ARE THESE ENEMIES?

MY OWN RELATIVES. THEY LIVE IN THE SAME WELL AS I DO.

OH! YOU LIVE IN A WELL! HOW AM I TO GET IN. AND EVEN IF I DID, WHERE WOULD I PERCH WHILE KILLING YOUR ENEMIES? GET AWAY WITH YOU!

WAIT, MY FRIEND, I'LL SHOW YOU HOW TO GET INTO THE WELL. AND I'LL ALSO SHOW YOU A COMFORTABLE HOLE, A LITTLE ABOVE THE WATER, WHERE YOU CAN REST. PLEASE COME OUT.

THE SNAKE WAS DEEP IN THOUGHT FOR A WHILE.

I AM NO LONGER AS YOUNG AS I USED TO BE ONCE IN A WHILE I CATCH A MOUSE AND THAT TOO WITH DIFFICULTY. HIS OFFER IS TEMPTING.

WELL, GANGADATTA, I HAVE DECIDED TO COME WITH YOU! LEAD AND I'LL FOLLOW.

THANK YOU, MY FRIEND. BUT THERE'S ONE THING. YOU MUST SPARE MY OWN FAMILY AND EAT ONLY THOSE WHOM I TELL YOU TO EAT.

11

WHEN GANGADATTA IS NOT AROUND, I SHALL HELP MYSELF TO A FRIENDLY FROG OR TWO AS WELL.

WHEN GANGADATTA CAME TO SEE HIM —

I'VE EATEN ALL YOUR ENEMIES!

GOOD! NOW YOU MAY RETURN TO YOUR HOLE, THE WAY YOU CAME, MY FRIEND.

RETURN TO MY HOLE? YOU CAN'T BE SERIOUS. SOME OTHER SNAKE WOULD HAVE MOVED INTO IT THE VERY DAY I LEFT.

NO, MY FRIEND, I WILL HAVE TO STAY HERE. AND SINCE YOU TOOK ME OUT OF MY HOLE, IT IS YOUR DUTY TO FEED ME.

YOU MUST GIVE ME ONE FROG AT A TIME, FROM YOUR FRIENDS AND YOUR OWN FAMILY. IF YOU DON'T, I'LL EAT YOU ALL UP.

13

THE DAYS WENT BY, GANGADATTA HAD NO PLAN AND ALL THE FROGS IN THE WELL WERE EATEN. ALL BUT HIMSELF.

DEAR GANGADATTA, I'M HUNGRY. PLEASE FIND ME SOMETHING TO EAT. IT'S YOUR DUTY TO DO SO.

THIS IS MY CHANCE TO ESCAPE.

MY FRIEND, AS LONG AS I'M ALIVE YOU WON'T GO HUNGRY. PERMIT ME TO LEAVE THIS WELL AND I'LL BRING YOU ALL THE FROGS FROM OTHER WELLS.

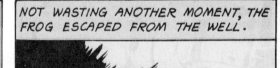

YOU, WHO HAVE BEEN LIKE A BROTHER TO ME, I'LL NEVER EAT NOW. IF YOU DO AS YOU PROMISE, YOU WILL BE LIKE A FATHER TO ME.

NOT WASTING ANOTHER MOMENT, THE FROG ESCAPED FROM THE WELL.

I'D BETTER FIND MYSELF ANOTHER WELL TO LIVE IN.

MEANWHILE, THE SNAKE WAITED IN VAIN FOR HIS RETURN.

I SHOULD NOT HAVE LET HIM GO.

MANY DAYS LATER, THE OLD SNAKE TURNED TO A LIZARD WHO LIVED IN THE SAME WELL.

MADAM, YOU AND GANGADATTA ARE OLD FRIENDS. PLEASE FIND HIM AND ASK HIM TO RETURN QUICKLY. NEVER MIND IF HE CAN'T GET OTHER FROGS TO COME.

TELL HIM THAT I WILL NOT HURT HIM; THAT I CAN'T LIVE WITHOUT HIM.

AFTER HUNTING IN ALL THE NEIGH-BOURING WELLS, THE LIZARD AT LAST FOUND THE FROG-KING.

DEAR GANGADATTA, WHAT ARE YOU DOING HERE? YOUR FRIEND, PRIYADARSHANA IS ANXIOUSLY AWAITING YOUR RETURN. HE PROMISES NOT TO HARM YOU. SO COME HOME.

A STARVING MAN IS NOT TO BE TRUSTED. I'VE LEARNT MY LESSON. HE WILL NEVER SEE ME AGAIN.

MORAL: DON'T CUT OFF YOUR NOSE TO SPITE YOUR FACE.

THE LION, THE JACKAL AND THE DONKEY

IN A JUNGLE THERE ONCE LIVED A LION WHO HAD A JACKAL FOR A SERVANT. WHENEVER THE LION KILLED AN ANIMAL, HE WOULD FIRST HAVE HIS FILL...

...AND LEAVE THE REST FOR THE JACKAL.

ONE DAY, THE LION MADE THE MISTAKE OF ATTACKING A FIERCE KING-ELEPHANT.

THE ELEPHANT WOUNDED HIM SO BADLY THAT HE COULD BARELY WALK.

FOR A WEEK, MASTER AND SERVANT STARVED. AT LAST, THE LION HAD AN IDEA.

IF YOU CAN BRING SOME ANIMAL TO ME WHICH I CAN KILL WITHOUT MUCH EFFORT, WE WON'T HAVE TO STARVE.

THE JACKAL SLOWLY ROSE TO HIS FEET AND SET OUT.

THAT'S A FINE DEER BUT TOO FAST FOR MY WOUNDED MASTER.

A FEW HOURS LATER —

AH! A DONKEY! JUST THE ANIMAL, I AM LOOKING FOR!

GOOD DAY UNCLE! WHY DO YOU LOOK SO FEEBLE?

HOW ELSE WOULD I LOOK, DEAR NEPHEW? I HAVE A CRUEL, MISERLY DHOBI FOR A MASTER. I AM OVERWORKED AND UNDERFED.

NOT A HANDFUL OF RICH FODDER HAVE I EATEN IN AGES! ALL THAT I LIVE ON IS THIS DRY GRASS.

17

THE TERRIFIED DONKEY TOOK ONE LOOK AT THE LION...

...AND RAN FOR HIS LIFE.

A STUPID DONKEY AND YOU COULDN'T KILL HIM! O MASTER, HOW DID YOU DARE ATTACK AN ELEPHANT?

IT'S NOT MY FAULT. I WASN'T READY FOR HIM. I DIDN'T EXPECT YOU TO RETURN SO SOON.

THEN BE READY NOW. I'LL GO AND BRING HIM BACK.

BRING HIM BACK? IMPOSSIBLE! HE SAW ME AND RAN AWAY. YOU'LL HAVE TO BRING SOME OTHER ANIMAL.

I WILL BRING BACK THAT VERY DONKEY. BE READY FOR HIM THIS TIME.

WHEN THE JACKAL WENT BACK TO THE DONKEY—

SO YOU'RE BACK! A FINE SPOT YOU TOOK ME TO! IT'S MY LUCK THAT I ESCAPED FROM THAT HORRIBLE CREATURE!

THE JACKAL LAUGHED.

UNCLE, THAT WAS A LOVESICK SHE-DONKEY. WHEN SHE SAW YOU, SHE SPRANG FORWARD TO WELCOME YOU. BUT YOU WERE SHY AND RAN AWAY.

YOU MUST COME BACK AND MARRY HER. IF YOU DON'T, SHE SAYS SHE'LL STARVE HERSELF TO DEATH.

SHE CAN'T BEAR TO BE SEPARATED FROM YOU. SO HAVE MERCY ON HER AND RETURN. IF YOU DON'T, YOU WILL BE GUILTY OF KILLING A LADY AND KAMADEVA* WILL BE ANGRY WITH YOU.

BELIEVING ALL THAT THE JACKAL SAID, THE FOOLISH DONKEY WENT BACK WITH HIM TO THE JUNGLE.

WONDER OF WONDERS! HE HAS BROUGHT HIM BACK! THIS TIME I WON'T FAIL HIM.

WHEN THEY WERE NEAR ENOUGH—

DIDN'T I TELL YOU I WOULD SUCCEED IF I WERE READY? NOW GUARD THIS DONKEY WHILE I GO TO BATHE.

* GOD OF LOVE

21

I CANNOT WAIT TILL HE RETURNS. WHILE HE IS AWAY, I'LL EAT UP THE DONKEY'S HEART AND EARS.

WHEN THE LION RETURNED, HE BEGAN SNIFFING AT THE DONKEY. SUDDENLY, HE BEGAN TO ROAR.

YOU SCOUNDREL! YOU HAVE EATEN THE EARS AND HEART! AM I TO EAT YOUR LEAVINGS?

BUT THE JACKAL WAS NOT FRIGHTENED. CALMLY HE FACED THE LION.

O KING, THIS CREATURE WAS BORN WITHOUT EARS OR HEART. IF NOT, WOULD HE HAVE COME HERE, HEARD YOUR ROAR, RUN AWAY IN TERROR...

...AND THEN COME BACK AGAIN?

WHAT HE SAYS MUST BE TRUE. OR ELSE WHY SHOULD THE DONKEY HAVE COME BACK?

ALL RIGHT. I SHALL FIRST HAVE MY FILL OF THIS DONKEY. YOU MAY THEN EAT THE REST.

MORAL: DON'T LOSE YOUR HEAD IN THE FACE OF CALAMITIES AND YOU'LL OVER- COME THEM.

THE DHOBI'S* DONKEY

SHUDDHAPATA, THE DHOBI, LOVED HIS DONKEY BUT COULD NOT AFFORD TO FEED IT WELL.

ONE DAY, AS HE WAS RETURNING HOME THROUGH A THICK JUNGLE, THE DONKEY STUMBLED UNDER ITS LOAD, SO WEAK HAD IT BECOME.

MY POOR FEEBLE BEAST! IF ONLY I COULD GIVE YOU BETTER FODDER!

WHAT'S THAT?

OH! A DEAD TIGER! THANK GOD IT WASN'T A LIVE ONE!

* WASHERMAN

HE WAS ABOUT TO WALK ON, BUT SUDDENLY STOPPED.

THAT'S IT! I'LL FLAY THIS FELLOW AND TAKE THE SKIN HOME. MY DONKEY WILL NO LONGER LACK FOOD.

YOU WILL SOON BECOME A FEARFUL TIGER, MY GENTLE DONKEY, AND EAT ALL THE MILLET YOU WANT.

THERE! NOW, IN THIS GARB, GO INTO THE MILLET FIELDS AT NIGHT.

THAT NIGHT —

COME. IT'S TIME FOR YOU TO CHANGE.

THE DHOBI THEN LED HIM TO THE MILLET FIELDS.

GO, MY PET, AND EAT TO YOUR HEART'S CONTENT. I'LL COME BACK FOR YOU IN THE MORN-ING.

AN HOUR LATER, WHEN THE FARMER AND HIS MEN CAME TO MAKE THEIR USUAL ROUNDS—

THERE'S AN ANIMAL IN THE MILLET FIELD!

IT'S A TIGER! RUN!

AND THE DONKEY MUNCHED AWAY UNDISTURBED.

IN THE MORNING, THE DHOBI LED HIM HOME. THIS WENT ON FOR MANY DAYS.

YOU'VE GROWN SO PLUMP, MY DONKEY. IF YOU GROW ANY PLUMPER, YOU WILL NOT BE ABLE TO ENTER YOUR STALL.

ONE NIGHT—

THERE HE IS AGAIN!

WHAT SHALL WE DO? WE'RE HELPLESS.

JUST THEN, THE DONKEY HEARD THE BRAY OF A SHE-DONKEY.

WE'VE BEEN DUPED. IT'S ONLY A DONKEY IN DISGUISE!

THE ANGRY FARMER AND HIS MEN CHARGED AT THE DONKEY AND BEAT HIM TO DEATH.

IN THE MORNING, THE DHOBI WAS SHOCKED TO SEE HIS DONKEY DEAD.

ALAS, MY FRIEND! HOW DID IT HAPPEN?

MORAL: SILENCE IS GOLDEN.

THE LIONESS AND THE JACKAL CUB

A LIONESS ONCE GAVE BIRTH TO TWO CUBS AND FOR A TIME COULD NOT GO OUT HUNTING.

SO HER HUSBAND WENT OUT...

...AND BROUGHT HOME THE GAME HE KILLED.

ONE DAY, HE COULD NOT FIND AN ANIMAL TO KILL. AS HE WAS RETURNING HOME —

WHAT'S THAT? A JACKAL CUB?

HE RAISED HIS PAW TO STRIKE IT WHEN PITY FOR THE TINY CREATURE OVERCAME HIM.

NO! HE'S JUST A CUB.

HOW CAN I KILL HIM?

PICKING THE CUB UP GENTLY WITH HIS TEETH...

...HE TOOK IT HOME ALIVE.

WHAT HAVE YOU BROUGHT TODAY?

I COULDN'T FIND A SINGLE ANIMAL. THEN I SAW THIS CUB. I DIDN'T HAVE THE HEART TO KILL HIM.

BUT YOU MAY KILL AND EAT HIM IF YOU LIKE.

WHEN YOU DIDN'T HAVE THE HEART TO KILL HIM, HOW CAN I?

HE SHALL GROW UP AS MY THIRD SON.

THE THREE CUBS SOON GREW PLUMP AND FRISKY.

YOU ARE FOOLS. I SHOULD HAVE LET THAT ELEPHANT KILL YOU. I WISH I HADN'T WARNED YOU. I...

CALM DOWN, MY SON. LET US GO OUTSIDE. I WANT TO TALK TO YOU.

WHEN THEY WERE ALONE —

YOU MUST NEVER AGAIN SPEAK LIKE THAT TO THEM. THEY ARE YOUR OLDER BROTHERS.

SO WHAT? DO YOU THINK I AM INFERIOR TO THEM IN ANY WAY? WHY DO THEY MAKE FUN OF ME? I'M GOING TO KILL THEM!

THE LIONESS HELD BACK THE SMILE THAT CAME TO HER LIPS.

POOR CUB. I WILL HAVE TO TELL HIM THE TRUTH— BEFORE IT'S TOO LATE.

MY CUB, YOU ARE THE SON OF A JACKAL. I BROUGHT YOU UP BECAUSE YOU WERE HELPLESS.

AS LONG AS MY SONS ARE CUBS, THEY WILL NOT HARM YOU. RUN AWAY AND JOIN YOUR OWN PACK BEFORE THEY KNOW YOU TO BE A JACKAL.

IF YOU DON'T, MY SONS WILL SOONER OR LATER FIGHT YOU AND KILL YOU.

THE POOR JACKAL WAS SO TERRIFIED WHEN HE HEARD THIS, THAT WITHOUT A WORD HE SLUNK AWAY TO FIND HIS OWN PACK.

MORAL: YOU ARE BEST OFF WITH YOUR OWN KIND.

AMAR CHITRA KATHA

Special volumes that bring the most popular classics of all time in a collector's edition.

Also available

- Devotees and Demons- 1
- Tulsidas' Ramayana
- Dasha Avatar
- Mahatma Gandhi
- Mahabharata (43-comic edition)
- Bhagawat

All titles available on www.amarchitrakatha.com.

THE DULLARD

TALES FROM THE PANCHATANTRA

The route to your roots

THE DULLARD

The 'dullard' of the story, an unfortunate failure at school, is a familiar figure in every age. Poor at his books, he compensates with a wealth of common sense, and goes on to survive life's trials rather well. His comically smug, scholarly companions, on the other hand, soon meet their doom. These tales may mirror everyday human vices in a time-tested and engaging way, but they are also gentle guides to a wiser, happier path.

This collection is based on Durgasimha's Kannada Panchatantra

Script
Kamala Chandrakant

Illustrations
Pradeep Sathe

Editor
Anant Pai

THE DULLARD

THERE WERE ONCE FOUR BRAHMANS WHO HAD GROWN UP TOGETHER IN THE SAME VILLAGE. THREE OF THEM SPENT ALL THEIR TIME PORING OVER SCHOLARLY TEXTS, BUT NOT SO THE FOURTH.

ONE DAY—

WHY DON'T WE TRAVEL TO THE CITY? WE COULD MAKE USE OF OUR LEARNING AND COLLECT A FORTUNE.

NOT A BAD IDEA. BUT WE'RE NOT TAKING THAT DULLARD WITH US. HE'D ONLY BE A BURDEN.

YOU'RE RIGHT. HE DOESN'T KNOW A THING!

HOW COULD YOU BE SO UNKIND! HE'S GROWN UP WITH US. WE CAN'T LEAVE HIM BEHIND. HE'LL SHARE WHAT WE MAKE.

OH! ALL RIGHT! LET HIM COME.

AND SO THE FOUR SET OUT.

2

3

MORAL: MERE SCHOLARSHIP WITHOUT COMMON SENSE IS FUTILE.

THE GREEDY BARBER

MANIBHADRA THE MERCHANT WAS VIRTUOUS, RICH AND GENEROUS.

MEN FLOCKED TO HIS HOME TO ENJOY HIS HOSPITALITY.

THEN ONE DAY, BY MAKING A BAD INVESTMENT HE LOST ALL HIS WEALTH; AND CONSEQUENTLY HIS FRIENDS.

HOW CAN I BLAME THEM? EVEN IF THEY DID COME IN, WHAT COULD I OFFER THEM?

MY KINDNESS? MY NOBILITY? MY LOVE? WHAT ARE THEY WORTH? NOTHING!

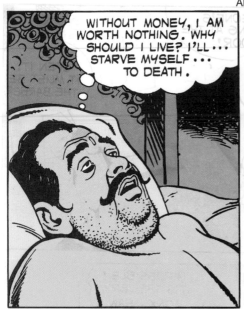

WITHOUT MONEY, I AM WORTH NOTHING. WHY SHOULD I LIVE? I'LL... STARVE MYSELF... TO DEATH.

AS THE MERCHANT FELL ASLEEP HE HAD AN AMAZING DREAM.

A GOOD MAN LIKE YOU MUST LIVE. I WILL COME TO YOUR DOOR TOMORROW IN THIS FORM.

TOUCH ME ON MY HEAD WITH A STICK AND I'LL TURN INTO GOLD; MORE GOLD THAN YOU COULD USE IN THIS LIFETIME.

THE NEXT MORNING—

WHAT A DREAM THAT WAS! WILL IT COME TRUE?

OF COURSE, NOT. IT WON'T. IT'S BECAUSE I WORRY DAY AND NIGHT ABOUT MONEY THAT I DREAMT ABOUT IT TOO.

8

9

THEIR CRIES CAUGHT THE ATTENTION OF THE CITY GUARDS.

THE MONGOOSE AND THE BRAHMAN'S WIFE

A KIND BRAHMAN ONCE FOUND A BABY MONGOOSE WHINING NEAR ITS DEAD MOTHER.

YOU POOR THING. I'LL TAKE YOU HOME WITH ME.

MY DEAR, YOU'LL HAVE TO BRING UP THIS LITTLE BABY, TOO.

WHY NOT! I LOVE LITTLE ONES. BRING HIM HERE.

THE WEE, HELPLESS MONGOOSE...

... SOON GREW INTO A PLUMP, STRONG CREATURE WITH SHARP TEETH.

MORAL: ACT IN HASTE, REPENT AT LEISURE.

THE WHEEL-BEARER

FOUR FRIENDS ONCE MADE THEIR WAY . . .

. . . TO THE REMOTE HERMITAGE OF YOGI BHAIRAVANANDA.

WHY HAVE YOU COME HERE?

WE SEEK YOUR HELP AND GUIDANCE. WE KNOW THAT YOU ARE GIFTED WITH STRANGE POWERS.

WE HAVE COME OUT OF OUR HOMES TO FIND SOME GOLD OR DIE IN THE ATTEMPT.

WE ARE CERTAIN THAT WHAT FOOLS CALL FATE OR LUCK IS ONLY THE FRUIT OF SINCERE EFFORT.

THEY SEEM TO BE COURAGEOUS AND DETERMINED. THEY SHOULD MAKE GOOD DISCIPLES.

I THINK I'LL HELP THEM. I HOPE THEY DON'T HAVE TO REGRET IT!

HE WENT INTO HIS HUT AND CAME OUT WITH FOUR COTTON WICKS.

I'LL GIVE EACH OF YOU ONE OF THESE WICKS.

TAKE THEM AND WALK TO THE MOUNTAINS. THE MOMENT A WICK FALLS, DIG THE GROUND AND YOU'LL FIND SOME TREASURE. COLLECT IT AND GO HOME.

THE FOUR FRIENDS BOUGHT SOME PICKAXES AND SET OUT.

WHATEVER WE FIND, WE'LL SHARE EQUALLY AMONG US.

AS THEY NEARED THE SLOPES OF THE MOUNTAINS —

HEY! THE WICK SLIPPED OUT OF MY HAND!

QUICK! LET'S DIG UP THE TREASURE.

KEEPING THE WICKS IN THEIR SLING-BAGS, THE OTHER THREE HELPED HIM.

LOOK! COPPER ORE! COME ALL OF YOU. LET'S CARRY AS MUCH AS WE CAN AND GO HOME.

FOOL! IT'S ONLY COPPER.

HOW MUCH CAN IT FETCH US?

LET'S GO FARTHER.

YOU MAY GO FARTHER IF YOU LIKE. I'M CONTENT WITH THIS. I'M RETURNING HOME.

WHAT ARE YOU DOING HERE WITH THAT WHEEL ON YOUR HEAD? ANYWAY CAN YOU TELL ME WHERE I COULD GET SOME WATER?

I'LL TELL YOU WHAT. YOU GO AHEAD. I'LL WAIT HERE FOR YOU.

BUT WE STILL HAVE ONE WICK LEFT. IT'S BOUND TO BRING US PRECIOUS GEMS. A HANDFUL OF WHICH WOULD FETCH US MORE THAN ALL THIS GOLD WOULD. COME. FOLLOW ME.

SO THE FOURTH FRIEND WALKED ON, ALONE.

IT'S A HOT DAY INDEED! THE SUN IS MERCILESS. BUT I MUST NOT GIVE UP.

OH, WHAT I WOULDN'T GIVE FOR A DROP OF WATER! RIGHT NOW IT SEEMS MORE PRECIOUS TO ME THAN THE MOST PRECIOUS OF GEMS.

HE WALKED ON AND ON BUT THE WICK REFUSED TO FALL.

I SEEM TO HAVE LOST MY WAY! WHATEVER I DO, I SEEM TO BE WALKING IN CIRCLES. WHERE AM I?

AA-A-AH!

MORAL: BE AMBITIOUS, BUT NOT AVARICIOUS.

EKABUDDHI

TWO FISH NAMED SHATABUDDHI AND SAHASRABUDDHI, A FROG NAMED EKABUDDHI AND HIS WIFE, ALL LIVED TOGETHER IN A SHALLOW POND.

ONE EVENING, TWO FISHERMEN HAPPENED TO PASS BY THE POND.

LOOK! LOOK AT THOSE BEAUTIES! LET'S GET TO WORK AND CATCH THEM.

NOT NOW. IT'S GETTING DARK. WE'LL COME BACK IN THE MORNING.

DID YOU HEAR THAT? WE'D BETTER FLEE FROM HERE.

CERTAINLY NOT. WE'LL STAY ON. ANYTHING CAN HAPPEN. THEY MIGHT NOT COME TOMORROW.

SUPPOSE THEY DO COME?

IF THEY DO, I KNOW A THOUSAND TRICKS BY WHICH I CAN SAVE ALL FOUR OF US.

MORAL: PREVENTION IS BETTER THAN CURE.

THE LAZY BRAHMAN

THERE WAS ONCE A LAZY BRAHMAN WHO LIVED SOLELY ON THE ALMS THAT HE COLLECTED. ONE DAY A KIND HOUSEWIFE GAVE HIM MORE FLOUR THAN HE NEEDED.

WHAT A STROKE OF LUCK! NOW I CAN GO RIGHT BACK HOME TO MY CHARPOY.

I'LL USE A LITTLE OF IT AND SAVE THE REST.

THERE! THAT SHOULD KEEP IT SAFE FROM THE RATS.

IF I SAVE THAT FLOUR TILL THERE IS A FAMINE IN THE LAND, I SHOULD GET QUITE SOME MONEY FOR IT.

"WITH THAT MONEY I'LL BUY A HE-GOAT AND A SHE-GOAT."

"SOON I'LL HAVE A FLOCK OF GOATS."

"I'LL SELL THOSE AND BUY A BULL AND A COW."

"WHEN THEY HAVE MULTIPLIED INTO A LARGE HERD..."

"...I'LL SELL THEM AND BUY MYSELF A PAIR OF BUFFALOES."

"WHEN THEY BREED, I'LL SELL THE LOT AND BUY A PAIR OF HORSES."

"SOON I'LL HAVE MANY HORSES. AND WITH ALL THE MONEY THEY'LL FETCH, I'LL BUY MYSELF A MANSION."

"SOME FATHER WILL OFFER HIS LOVELY DAUGHTER TO ME IN MARRIAGE."

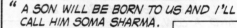

"A SON WILL BE BORN TO US AND I'LL CALL HIM SOMA SHARMA.

"SOON HE'LL BEGIN TO CRAWL."

"I'LL BE WORRIED THAT THE HORSES WILL TRAMPLE HIM."

AMAR CHITRA KATHA

5-IN-1

Five theme-based titles in every collection

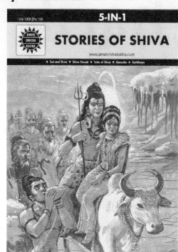

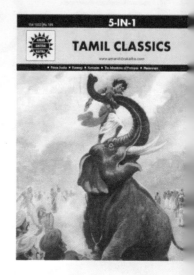

Hard-bound editions that every generation will cherish

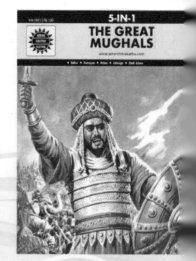